Where Next, Dinky?

Written by Patricia Toht

Illustrated by Erin Brown

Jia and Dinky Dragon travelled together.
They were in England with Auntie,
touring London on a bus.

TOUR BUS

"Dragons like to see," Dinky grumbled.
He wiggled out to peek when ...

2

RUMBLE!

The bus moved.

BUMP!

It hit a hole, and **down**

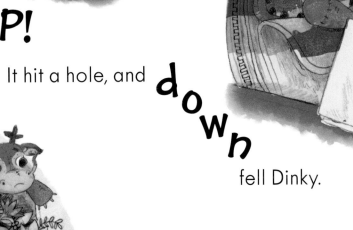

fell Dinky.

"Oh, dear!" he said.

He landed in the flowers of a fancy hat.

"Dragons don't like getting lost," Dinky said. He pulled a United Kingdom map from his pocket.

He marked his map.

Where's Jia?

Dinky gripped the hat as the woman hurried to a train station.

"West to Wales, platform five!" an announcement called.

She dashed into a carriage, and — **clickety-clack** — they sped away. Dinky watched hills climb and fall.

4

Soon, a conductor called:
"Cardiff! All change!"

Dinky marked his map.

Is Jia here, too?

5

"Gran!" voices called.
"This way!"

Gran joined her family at a festival by a bay.

"Dragons don't like fairground rides," Dinky said.

6

Whoa!

They dipped.

Whoops!

He slipped, and

down

fell Dinky.

"Oh, dear!" he said.

He dropped onto a bag at a nearby café. Dinky scooted inside the bag, just as a woman grabbed it.

Dinky gazed through a giant window. Aeroplanes lined up outside. A sign said:

TO BELFAST

"Dragons like to fly!" Dinky said. They boarded, and — WHOOSH! — lifted into the sky.

The pilot said, "Welcome to all passengers. Today we are flying north, to Belfast in Northern Ireland."

Dinky marked his map, and soon they landed.

Can you find me, Jia?

They left the airport, and the woman rushed along. Suddenly …

Oops!

… she stumbled.

POP!

Her bag opened wide, and

d
o
w
n

fell Dinky.

"Oh, dear!" he said.

"A wee dragon!"

A girl tucked Dinky into her hoodie.

She walked with her dad into a huge museum. As they visited the rooms inside, more people joined their tour.

"Dragons don't like crowds," Dinky complained, ducking down.

When he peered out again, they were in a car. A sign said:

FERRY – EAST

TO SCOTLAND

The car rolled onto the boat and
— **SPLASH!** — they pushed out to sea.

"Dragons like boats," Dinky said.
He watched the city shrink
behind them, and a tiny town
grow in front.

They docked and drove on. Hours later, they
entered Edinburgh. Dinky marked his map.

Dad carried the sleeping
girl from the car to bed.
Dinky huddled in her
hoodie and slept,
dreaming of Jia.

11

The next day, they strolled to a park that curved beside a rocky cliff. A castle perched above.

Dinky held on as the girl raced along the path. Then ...

BOOM!

A castle cannon blasted.

Oh!

The girl jumped, and

d
o
w
n

fell Dinky.

"Oh, dear!" he said.

Where am I?

He toppled into fabric that felt like dragon wings. Thin metal bars trapped him like a cage.

"Dragons don't like cages," Dinky said. A tear rolled down his snout.

"South ..." a man above him muttered.

The cage moved. Soon Dinky heard:

Clickety-clack!
Clickety-clack!

13

When the **clickety-clack** stopped, they walked on.
When they paused, Dinky heard traffic rushing by.

"We've looked everywhere," someone nearby said.

"I **must** find him before I leave,
Auntie!" a familiar voice answered.

LONDON BRIDGE 17

Jia!

Dinky struggled to get out. Then he
heard a **pitter-patter.**

"It's starting to rain," said Auntie,
"and I've forgotten my umbrella!"

"I'll share," the man said.

14

UP! The cage rose.

FWOOP!

It opened, and **down** fell Dinky . . . into Jia's arms!

"Dinky!" Jia said. "Where have you been?"

She spotted the map in his pocket and opened it.

"Oh, I've missed you!" Jia hugged him.

Dragons LOVE hugs and Dinky loves Jia!

Published by Pearson Education Limited, 80 Strand, London, WC2R 0RL.

www.pearsonschools.co.uk

Text © Pearson Education Limited 2020

Written by Patricia Toht

Project managed and edited by Just Content Limited

Original illustrations © Pearson Education Limited 2020

Illustrated by Erin Brown

Designed and typeset by Collaborate Agency Limited

First published 2020

23 22 21

10 9 8 7 6 5 4 3 2

British Library Cataloguing in Publication Data

A catalogue record for this book is available from the British Library

ISBN 978 0 435 20120 3

Printed in Slovakia by Neografia

Note from the publisher

Pearson has robust editorial processes, including answer and fact checks, to ensure the accuracy of the content in this publication, and every effort is made to ensure this publication is free of errors. We are, however, only human, and occasionally errors do occur. Pearson is not liable for any misunderstandings that arise as a result of errors in this publication, but it is our priority to ensure that the content is accurate. If you spot an error, please do contact us at resourcescorrections@pearson.com so we can make sure it is corrected.

The Sleepy
Shepherd

Acknowledgements

This book began life a long time ago as a story told in a school assembly
and at a Christmas crib service. It grew and changed over the years,
and I only wrote it down recently. I wasn't sure how to get it into print,
so am hugely grateful to Alison Barr at SPCK for her commitment
to the story and her hard work in getting it published. Chris Hagan's
wonderful illustrations have also vividly brought the story to life.
My wife Rebecca and my three sons, Joseph, Benjamin and Samuel,
were early critics of the story. Children at Moulsham Junior School and
Margaretting Church of England Primary School also read a draft of
it and made several helpful suggestions. Miranda Ball read the final
version and gave it the thumbs up. I am grateful to them all.

First published in Great Britain in 2018

Society for Promoting Christian Knowledge
36 Causton Street
London SW1P 4ST
www.spck.org.uk

Text copyright © Stephen Cottrell 2018
Illustrations copyright © Chris Hagan 2018

British Library Cataloguing-in-Publication Data
A catalogue record for this book is available from the British Library

ISBN 978-0-281-07802-8

1 3 5 7 9 10 8 6 4 2

Typeset and designed by Anna Lubecka, Banana Bear Books
First printed in India by Thomson Press

Produced on paper from sustainable forests

The Sleepy Shepherd

A timeless retelling of the Christmas story

Stephen Cottrell

Illustrated by Chris Hagan

This is the story of Silas the sleepy shepherd.

Silas was the sleepiest person ever.

He worked as a shepherd boy in the fields around Bethlehem, but while the other shepherds carefully watched their flocks, it was more than likely that Silas would be curled up under a tree, fast asleep.

It had always been like this. Silas was just one of those people who never seemed to have enough sleep.

He would doze off after breakfast, even though he had only just got up! Eating really was very tiring, so afterwards didn't everyone need a little rest?

He would have another nap in the middle of the morning.

He would disappear for forty winks after lunch.

He liked a siesta in the afternoon.

All through the day, and at every opportunity, Silas would sneak off, find a corner to himself, check to see that no one was around and nod off to sleep.

When he was at school, he used to fall asleep during the lessons.

When he played with his friends, he would nod off halfway through a game.

Once, he even fell asleep while he was eating dinner. He just went out like a light. His head fell forward and dropped right into the middle of his food. To the utter amazement of everyone else round the table, there he stayed for the rest of the meal. Snoring gently. Dreaming sweetly. No wonder he was called the 'sleepy shepherd'.

The other shepherds were at their wits' end. Even though he was just a boy and they hoped he would grow out of it, Silas made them cross. They needed him to do his share of the work. They needed him to learn the ways of a good shepherd.

Sometimes they teased him. Sometimes they said that, if he didn't buck his ideas up, he would lose his job. Sometimes they didn't know what to do, so one of them would poke him with his staff every time he dropped off – which, as you will have gathered, was quite often! It seemed that every time their backs were turned Silas would fall asleep.

At night it was even worse.

Sometimes the shepherds had to stay up all through the night. When it was dark, a wolf or a bear might break into the flock and snatch away one of their sheep or even one of the baby lambs. They needed to be especially vigilant, and they needed everyone's help.

Silas found it difficult enough to stay awake during the daytime, so at night he found it impossible. He would try singing songs. He would try jumping up and down on the spot. He would try pinching himself. Nothing worked – he couldn't keep awake. So, when one of the other shepherds asked him to check the flock by counting all the sheep . . . well, you can imagine what happened.

One winter's night, all the shepherds were out in the fields, watching their flocks. It was cold and still; a night when it seemed as if the sky was filled with more stars than ever before.

The sheep were restless. There was something in the air, but nobody knew what. 'We need to keep especially watchful tonight, Silas,' said an older shepherd. 'No falling asleep, do you hear?'

Silas nodded. He *wanted* to stay awake, but he was already feeling awfully drowsy. The waves of sleep were crashing over him. His eyes were feeling heavier and heavier.

He paced around the small enclosure where they kept the sheep. He had to try his best to stay awake.

The other shepherds were warming themselves by the fire. Silas looked over at them. The fire did look warm and inviting. It did look cosy. It did look peaceful. Well, the next thing that happened was this – I'm sure you can guess – Silas fell asleep. There and then, standing in the middle of the field, holding his staff, he just closed his eyes, his legs crumpled beneath him and he dropped off to sleep.

He was fast asleep.

Absolutely sound asleep.

Snug as a bug in a rug asleep.

In the middle of the field.

And there he stayed.

Right through the night.

Right through until morning.

Asleep.

But something else happened that night. Something wondrous.
Something amazing. Something the world had never seen before.
Something *so* wondrous and *so* amazing that the shepherds forgot about
Silas. Something *so* wondrous and *so* amazing that they even forgot about
their sheep.

All of a sudden, the sky was filled with light. Flashing, sweeping glowing rays, bright as daybreak, and all the colours of the rainbow. There were angels singing and rejoicing. 'Glory to God in the highest,' they sang, 'and peace to God's people on earth.' It was the sweetest sound you ever heard, as if the whole of heaven was singing. It was the brightest, most beautiful light. The shepherds stood there, gazing into the sky with amazement and wonder. Some of them even pinched themselves to check that they hadn't fallen asleep and were dreaming.

But it wasn't a dream. The angels said to them that a child was being born in Bethlehem that night, a new king, and they were invited to go to the town, where they would find the baby wrapped in swaddling bands and lying in a manger.

Compelled by the message from the angels, the shepherds left their sheep. They hurried down the hill into Bethlehem. There they found the baby and his mother, just as the angels had said. He had been born in a stable at the back of an inn. The baby's name was Jesus, his mother was Mary, and her husband was Joseph. The proud parents stood on each side of the manger where the baby lay. Even though the manager had been filled with fresh straw to keep the baby warm, it was still not much more than a feeding trough for the animals. Nevertheless, Mary and Joseph looked at the baby Jesus with tenderness and wonder, like every other new parent when a baby is born.

But this wasn't just any newborn baby. This child was God's Son. God with us, a new king, a saviour of the world, one who would bring peace on earth. Yes, that was what the angels had said: 'Peace on earth; good will to all people.' Breathless and filled with excitement, the shepherds gazed in wonder at the baby and spoke of all that the angels had told them.

Then, surrounded by Mary and Joseph and the animals in the stable, they were the first people to kneel and worship Jesus.

Outside, dawn was beginning to paint its friendly colours of light and warmth across the sky. Birds sang in the trees. The little town of Bethlehem began to stir. Remembering their sheep out in the fields, the shepherds said their goodbyes to Mary and Joseph, and each one of them kissed the baby Jesus on his forehead. Then they made their way back to the hills. They were full of joy.

As the shepherds walked along, they started singing. A few people told them to be quiet. One rather grumpy lady leaned out of her window and asked the shepherds if they knew what time it was! A man who was opening up his shop thought they had been drinking. Someone even threatened to throw a bucket of water over the shepherds if they didn't pipe down, but they just smiled back and told everyone they met about what had happened that night.

On the outskirts of the town, some children were playing. They weren't quite sure what to make of the shepherds as they came noisily

down the road. They were a little bit frightened. But when the shepherds pointed to the sky and told them about the angels singing and the sky filled with light, and when they said a new king had been born in a stable just behind them there in Bethlehem, the children became excited as well and they too ran to find the baby.

When the shepherds returned to their sheep, they remembered Silas. 'Where is he?' they thought. Surely even he couldn't have slept through everything? They called for him, but, of course, he was sound asleep so he didn't answer them. Along with the birdsong, they could hear something else. What was it? A snuffling and a gurgling sound? A sort of gentle snorting? Could it be a wolf or a bear coming after the sheep?

No. It was Silas snoring!

They found him glued to the spot where he had fallen asleep the night before. He hadn't moved at all. There he was, curled up in the middle of the field, sleeping like a log. As happy as a cat that's got the cream, snoring away! The shepherds prodded him gently with their staffs, but he didn't wake up. He just groaned softly, rolled over and continued sleeping. He was having some very sweet dreams.

'Oh, leave him be,' they said. 'He'll wake up when he's ready.'

So they didn't bother him, but instead stoked the fire and made themselves some breakfast.

Scrumptious and inviting aromas of toasting bread, grilled sausage and fresh fruit began to fill the morning air. As they wafted towards Silas, he began to stir. He was feeling hungry. He licked his lips. Was it morning already? That couldn't be right. He stretched his limbs and yawned. 'Oh dear,' he thought, 'it *is* morning and I've fallen asleep on the job *again!*'

Ashamed of himself, and anxious to avoid the rebuke of his friends, Silas stayed where he was in the long grass. He just couldn't face them. Snatches of their conversation drifted over on the breeze.

'Well, that was an amazing thing,' one of them said.

'The sky full of angels,' said another.

'I don't think I've ever seen anything so beautiful,' said a third.

'And such a *beautiful* baby!'

'A king born in a stable.'

'A royal birth in Bethlehem and *we* were the honoured guests! Can you believe it?'

Well, no, Silas couldn't. What were they on about?

Who was this baby they were referring to? What was all this about angels and stables?

It sounded a wonderful story, but as Silas listened, he felt sure that his friends were just making it up to get back at him. He had fallen asleep. Again. Now they had concocted this story to tease him. To cap it all, he heard one of them saying, 'We must tell Silas about this when he wakes up.'

23

'*If* he wakes up!' another butted in.

'I think he must have died,' another one said. 'He's been asleep *so* long this time!'

They all laughed, 'How could anyone sleep through all those angels singing?'

'That's it,' thought Silas. 'They *are* playing a trick on me. They want me to believe this story about angels and babies; and they want to see if I'll go down to Bethlehem and look round the stables for a baby there. Well, I won't give them the satisfaction. I *won't* go looking for any newborn kings. A newborn king in Bethlehem, indeed! Whoever heard such a story? Kings are born in *palaces,* not stables.' With that, Silas got up and joined his friends.

Of course, they told him all that had happened and all he'd missed, but try as they might, they couldn't convince him their story was true. Silas was just too stubborn. He folded his arms and refused to listen. 'Pull the other one!' he told them.

So Silas didn't go down to Bethlehem. He never did see the baby Jesus. He missed the excitement of that special night.

Although there have been lots of people who have never believed the story of Christmas, in many ways the story of Silas is the saddest, because he was there. He had a chance to see Jesus, but fell asleep, then he wouldn't believe his friends.

But, deep in his heart, Silas wondered.

What *had* happened that night?

Were there angels in the skies over Bethlehem, singing a song of peace and good will?

Was there a new king born in a manger?

Many years passed. Silas the sleepy shepherd boy grew up to be a man and came to have a wife and family of his own. He left the fields around Bethlehem and moved to the great city of Jerusalem, where there was more work to be found. He still dozed off a lot, though things got a bit better.

Still it wasn't easy. A reputation for falling asleep on the job didn't help! But after a while, he was hired to look after the goats of a wealthy man who owned a beautiful and mysterious garden on the edge of Jerusalem at a place called Gethsemane.

One spring, Jerusalem was in turmoil. There was a preacher from Nazareth called Jesus who had come to the city. He was speaking about God in a new way that was disturbing, but also beautiful. He rode into Jerusalem on a donkey and people waved palm branches before him and sang songs. He made everyone happy, but he also upset people when he overturned the tables of the money changers in the Temple. It was as if he thought we didn't need the Temple any more. He said that he came from God; that he was God's chosen one, God's Son. He said he had come to bring forgiveness and God's kingdom of peace on earth. Yes, those words rang a bell in Silas' heart: peace on earth, the rule of God – that was what this Jesus was coming to bring.

Jesus told lovely stories. He told stories that ordinary people could understand: stories about family disagreements, about unpredictable harvests and the dangers of the open road. The stories got passed on. Good stories always do. 'This is a fine way of teaching,' thought Silas.

There was one story that Silas particularly loved. It was about a lost sheep and a good shepherd. The shepherd had a hundred sheep, but when one of them went missing, he didn't just shrug his shoulders and say, 'Oh well, it's only one; I've still got ninety-nine others.' Rather, he left the ninety-nine to go in search of the one that had gone astray. When he found it, he carried it home, rejoicing. He was a good shepherd who cared about those who were lost.

Apparently, that was what Jesus called himself: a good shepherd.

Silas smiled when he heard this, because *he* wanted to be a good shepherd, but he had never quite managed it. He had always fallen asleep at the wrong time. In many ways, he was a bit lost himself.

The name, 'Jesus', was strangely familiar. It rang a bell in his heart.

Silas had heard it before, but he couldn't remember where . . .

It was a Thursday evening – a still, cool night, like another he remembered from long ago. Stars sparkled in an inky black sky. An owl hooted in the darkness, searching for its prey.

Silas was in the garden of Gethsemane, watching the few sheep and goats that he now looked after. He still found it hard to keep awake, but fortunately the animals were quite old and didn't wander far, and there was little danger in this peaceful place.

Silas was feeling very sleepy. Indeed, he was almost asleep when, suddenly, he heard voices. Some people were coming into the garden. They seemed agitated. Something was worrying them. They didn't see Silas, but he could hear and see them. One of them – their leader it seemed – said to the others that he was going to pray. He asked his followers to keep watch with him and to stay awake. Then he went and knelt down.

Silas heard the words of the man's prayer. He couldn't help it, the man was only a short distance away. Silas was in the shadows, though, so no one had seen him.

The man's prayers weren't like any that Silas had heard before. He was speaking to God in such an easy way, as a son talks to his father, but also pleading with God. He was saying, 'Please God, can there be another way? Please God, if it is possible, take this cup away from me!'

Silas didn't know what he meant, but he could see that the man was in pain. He could see that he looked lost. Silas knew how that felt.

Silas also saw something else that was very familiar. All the friends of this man, who were *supposed* to be keeping awake, had fallen asleep. They were just like him: sleeping on the job.

Silas smiled to himself. 'Why is it,' he thought, 'that so many of us never manage to do the things we want to do?'

Then he felt sorry for the man who was praying on his own. He seemed like a good person and he was obviously very anxious about something.

The man got up and went over to his friends. He was cross with them. 'Please,' he said, 'can you not watch with me for *one* hour?'

'I'm sorry,' said a follower. 'It's so late and we're so tired. Can't we just go home to bed, Jesus?'

It was then that Silas knew who the man was. This was the preacher from Nazareth, the man sent by God, the one who was causing such a stir. Then Silas remembered something else. He remembered that night when he was a boy. It all came rushing back to him. Of course, this was that baby born in Bethlehem. *His* name was Jesus. Here he was, grown into a man.

Silas realized that what his friends had told him all those years ago was true. There was a baby, born in a manger; God's Son, come to bring peace on earth.

Silas trembled with anticipation. At last he was seeing the person his friends had seen all those years before. He watched Jesus go back to his prayers. He watched the tears roll down his face as he spoke to God. He also saw his followers fall asleep once more.

It was then that Silas made a great decision. Now he could make amends for falling asleep all those years ago. Now he could be a good shepherd. Jesus wanted someone to watch with him; well, *he* could be that someone. He could watch with him; he could pray with him.

Silas crept a little closer. He was still too timid actually to go up to Jesus, and he could tell that he was deep in prayer, so he stayed in the shadows. He knelt down and, looking up to the heavens, he prayed that this man might be free from fear, he might be able to drink this cup that was being offered him and have the strength to do what he must do.

That night, Silas stayed awake. He stayed awake with Jesus. He watched and prayed. He prayed for the peace that the angels sang about; that it would come to earth through Jesus.

Well, that's the end of the story of Silas, but it is not the end of the story of Jesus. Later that night, Jesus was arrested. Silas stayed back in the shadows and watched the soldiers take him away. The next day, Jesus was killed. They hung him up on a cross and it seemed as if his prayer of peace had come to nothing, but two days later, something very, very amazing happened; something to turn the world upside down; something that made you look differently at everything.

God raised Jesus to life.

God showed the world a new hope and a new peace.

Silas was very sad when he heard that Jesus had died, but he was full of joy when he heard Jesus had risen again.

So this was the peace the angels sang about: the promise that death is not the end, things can change and, beyond death, there is a new life and a new hope.

'Well,' thought Silas, 'this really is worth staying awake for!'